BLESS ME,
ULTIMA

Rudolfo A. Anaya

WRITERS' VOICES

SIGNAL HILL

BLESS ME,
ULTIMA

Rudolfo A. Anaya

WRITERS' VOICES™ was made possible by grants from
The Booth Ferris Foundation, The Vincent Astor
Foundation, and The Scripps Howard Foundation.

• • •

ATTENTION READERS: We would like to hear what
you think about our books. Please send your comments
or suggestions to:

The Editors
New Readers Press
P.O. Box 131
Syracuse, NY 13210-0131

• • •

Selection: From BLESS ME, ULTIMA by Rudolfo A.
Anaya. Copyright © 1972 by Rudolfo A. Anaya. Reprinted
by permission of the author. Published by Tonatiuh-Quinto
Sol International Publishers, Berkeley, CA.

SIGNAL HILL

Additional material
© 1989 Signal Hill Publications
A publishing imprint of Laubach Literacy International

10 9 8 7 6 5 4 3 2

ISBN 1-929631-06-4

Designed by Paul Davis Studio

First printing: January 1989

The words "Writers' Voices" are a trademark of
New Readers Press.

Photo credits: Courtesy of Mark Nohl, Photographer, New Mexico
Economic Development & Tourism Department

PRINTED WITH
SOY INK™

This book was printed on 100% recycled paper
which contains 50% postconsumer waste.

Acknowledgments

We gratefully acknowledge the generous support of the following foundations and corporations that made the publication of WRITERS' VOICES and NEW WRITERS' VOICES possible: The Booth Ferris Foundation, The Vincent Astor Foundation, and the Scripps Howard Foundation. We also wish to thank Hildy Simmons, Linda L. Gillies, and David Hendin for their assistance.

This book could not have been realized without the kind and generous cooperation of the author, Rudolfo A. Anaya, and his publisher, Tonatiuh-Quinto Sol International. We are also grateful to Dr. Nicolás Kanellos for his help.

We deeply appreciate the contributions of the following suppliers: Cam Steel Die Rule Works, Inc. (steel cutting die for display); Domtar Industries Inc. (text stock); Federal Paper Board Company, Inc. and Milton Paper Company Inc. (cover stock); Jackson Typesetting (text typesetting); Lancer Graphic Industries Inc. (cover printing); Martin/Friess Communications (display header); Mergenthaler Container (corrugated display); Offset Paperback Mfrs., Inc., A Bertelsmann Company (text printing and binding); and Stevenson Photo Color Company (cover color separations).

Our thanks to Paul Davis Studio and Claudia Bruno, José Conde, Myrna Davis, Paul Davis, and Jeanine Esposito for the inspired design of the books and their covers. We would also like to thank Barbara A. Mancuso of *The New York Times* Pictures for her help with photo research and selection.

Contents

About *Writers' Voices*

"I want to read what others do—what I see people reading in libraries, on the subway, and at home."

Mamie Moore, a literacy student,
Brooklyn, New York

Writers' Voices is our response to Mamie Moore's wish:

the wish to step forward into the reading community,
the wish to have access to new information,
the wish to read to her grandchildren,
the wish to read for the joy of reading.

Note to the Reader

"What we are familiar with, we cease to see. The writer shakes up the familiar scene, and as if by magic, we see a new meaning in it."

Anaïs Nin

Writers' Voices invites you to discover new meaning. One way to discover new meaning is to learn something new. Another is to see in a new way something you already know. Writers touch us by writing about familiar things—love, family, death, for example. Even if the experiences in a book are different from our own, the emotions may be familiar. Our own thoughts and feelings let us interact with the author's story.

Writers' Voices is a series of books. Each book contains unedited selections from one writer's work. We chose the selections because the writers' voices can be clearly heard. Also, they deal with experiences that are interesting to think about and discuss.

If you are a new reader, you may want to have a selection read aloud to you, perhaps more than once. This will free you to enjoy the piece, to hear the language used, and to think about its meaning. Even if you are a more experienced reader, you may enjoy hearing the selection read aloud before reading it silently to yourself.

Each selection is set in a framework to expand your understanding of the selection. The framework includes a chapter that tells about the writer's life. Some authors write about their own lives; other authors write stories from their imagination. You may wonder why an author chose to write what he or she did. Sometimes you can find the answer by knowing about the author's life.

You may also find chapters about the characters, the plot, and when or where the story took place. These will help you begin thinking about the selection. They will also help you understand what may be unfamiliar to you.

We believe that to be a reader, you must be at the center of the reading process. We believe you learn best when you choose what you will read. We encourage you to read *actively*. An active reader does many things—while reading, and before and after reading—that help him or her better understand and enjoy a book. Here are some suggestions of things you can do:

Before Reading
- Read the front and back covers of the book, and look at the cover illustration. Think about what you expect the book to be about, based on this information.
- Think about why you want to read this book.
- Ask yourself what you want to discover, and what questions you hope will be answered.
- Think about how your own experiences and knowledge can help you better understand the book.

During Reading
- Try to stay with the rhythm of the language. If you find any words or sentences you don't understand, keep reading to see if the meaning becomes clear. If it doesn't, go back and reread the difficult part or discuss it with others. If you prefer to wait until you have read the whole story before you reread the difficult part, underline it so it will be easy to find later.
- Put yourself into the story. If you feel left out, ask why. Is it the writing? Is it something else?
- Ask yourself questions as you read. For example: Do I believe this story or this character? Why?

After Reading
- Ask yourself if the story makes you see any of your own experiences in a new way.
- Ask yourself if the story has given you any new information.
- Keep a journal in which you can

write down your thoughts about what you have read, and save new words you have learned.

- Discuss what you have read with others.

Good writing should make you think after you put the book down. Whether you are a beginning reader, a more experienced reader, or a teacher of reading, we encourage you to take time to think about these books and to discuss your thoughts with others.

When you finish a selection, you may want to choose among the questions and suggested activities that follow. They are meant to help you discover more about what you have read and how it relates to you—as a person, as a reader, and as a writer.

When you are finished with the book, we hope you will write to our editors about your reactions. We want to know your thoughts about our books, and what they have meant to you.

About Rudolfo A. Anaya

Rudolfo A. Anaya was born on October 30, 1937, in the small village of Pastura, New Mexico. Anaya has said, "Soon after I was born, we moved to Santa Rosa, which was on Highway 66. For me that road was the link between the East and the West. There was much life there. Santa Rosa is a geographical setting, in a sense, that I use to set the stage for *Bless Me, Ultima*. The river flows through the valley, and the highway and the railroad tracks dissect the town in another direction. And always there is the interplay of people on the stage of life with the elements of nature— and the llano [plain or flat ground] itself working through the people, changing the people, finally making the people who they are. I can't think of very many things that I have written that do not have a reference to those natural forces and that earth and people which nurtured me." (Bruce-Novoa 1980)

In 1952, Anaya and his family moved to the Barelas barrio in Albuquerque, New Mexico. In 1963, he graduated from the University of New Mexico. He worked at many jobs to help pay for school.

While Anaya was a student, he began to write novels. "People ask me why I became a writer. My answer is that I became a writer in my childhood. That is why that time has been so important to me. The characters of my childhood, the family, friends, and neighbors that made up my world, they and their lives fed my imagination. All cultural groups develop an oral tradition, and the tradition of the Mexican-Americans is immensely rich. The stories of characters, fanciful and real, constantly filled my life. In the circle of my own community, my imagination was nourished." (Sarkissian 1986)

Anaya worked on *Bless Me, Ultima* for seven years. He rewrote it completely six or seven times. It was his first published novel.

Today, Rudolfo A. Anaya is a professor at the University of New Mexico. He writes novels, short stories, and plays.

For the quotations, we used Bruce-Novoa, *Chicano Authors: Inquiry by Interview* (Austin, 1980) and Adele Sarkissian, ed., *Contemporary Authors Autobiography Series,* Volume 4 (Detroit, 1986).

About the Chicanos of
New Mexico

Bless Me, Ultima is a story about a Chicano family in New Mexico. This chapter provides a short historical background to the selection.

The first people to migrate to the Americas came from Asia thousands of years ago. They settled in many parts of North and Central America.

Ancient Central American societies were very advanced. They had a great deal of knowledge about science and religion. They built palaces and temples, and created beautiful art. One of the best known of these people were the Aztecs.

The Aztecs came to Mexico from Aztlan around 1168. Aztlan was in North America, but no one, today, knows exactly where it was located.

They built a large and beautiful city

in the Valley of Mexico (where Mexico City is today). They fought and conquered the other cities around them. Their empire grew to five million people.

The Aztecs were known as traders. They traded gold, silver, and precious stones. They also traded fruits, vegetables, and beautiful woven material.

Religion was part of their daily life and their priests were very important. The Aztecs built temple pyramids where they made human sacrifices to the gods. They believed that all creatures and things were part of a natural cycle of life and death. Sacrifice was a part of this natural cycle.

The Aztecs were at the peak of their power when the first people from Spain arrived in Mexico in 1519 (Mexico is an Aztec word meaning "place of the war god"). Their leader was Hernando Cortez. The Aztec ruler was Montezuma.

At first, the Spaniards said that they had come in peace. But two years later, the Spaniards destroyed the Aztec city and killed hundreds of thousands of people. They burned many of the books in Aztec libraries and stole their precious objects.

The Spaniards changed the name of the land from Mexico to Nueva España (New Spain). They took over more and more land, killing many more native peoples. The Spaniards forced the people to convert to their Roman Catholic religion. They used the native people and their land to become rich. The descendants of these Spanish explorers and the native Mexicans are the ancestors of today's Chicanos.

In 1598, Don Juan de Onate led 130 families and a large herd of livestock from Nueva España to an area that they named "New Mexico." He was of Spanish descent. His wife was Montezuma's great-granddaughter. He claimed the land and all the native peoples living on it for Spain.

The Native Americans in New Mexico were either farmers who lived in villages, or hunters who roamed the land. The people from Nueva España settled near the Native Americans and raised livestock.

New Mexico had good land for farming and it also had good land for ranching. The people who lived on farms grew food for the people who lived on the ranches. The farmers lived in small towns. The ranchers lived on the plains. They followed their cattle and sheep from place to place on horseback.

In 1810, the people of Nueva España revolted against Spain. In 1821, they won the war and became the independent nation of Mexico.

In 1846, the United States went to war with Mexico. The United States won in 1848 and got all of northern Mexico. New Mexico was a part of this land and became a territory of the United States.

• • •

Until then, land in New Mexico had been owned by communities, as well as by individuals. As more and more people from the eastern United States arrived, they took land away from the New Mexicans for big farms. The large ranches and farms were fenced in. The government also took a lot of land on which to build railroads.

The small farmers had lived in towns and had shared land where they let their small flocks of sheep graze. Much of this land also was taken by the government and easterners, and the sheep could no longer graze there.

The small farmers could not compete with the big farmers. Many of the small farmers had to go to work for the big farmers, or take jobs in towns.

A small farmer's life was hard but he and his family felt very close to the land. They grew their crops, kept sheep and pigs for food, and had a cow for milk. They used a horse to help in the fields.

The big ranchers hired *vaqueros* (cowboys) to manage their herds. Many of them were descended from the first Mexican settlers. They lived a hard and rough life, riding over the plains in the day, sleeping under the open sky at night. They would be away from their families for days at a time. Their horses were their companions and most important possessions.

In 1912, New Mexico became a state. There were many more changes in the way the New Mexican people lived. The growth of big farms and ranches continued. Mining and lumbering grew. Factories were built and many people moved to the growing cities.

Many of the Chicanos and Native Americans whose ancestors had been the original settlers did not benefit from any of these changes. Many of them had lost their land and their heritage. Yet, their proud traditions stayed with them. And the fabric of their culture remained rich and strong.

About the Selection from
Bless Me, Ultima

Bless Me, Ultima is the story of Antonio, his family, and the wise, old woman named Ultima who came to live with them. The story is set in Guadalupe, New Mexico, a small town near the *llano* (plain). Antonio lives with his father, mother, and two sisters. He has three older brothers who are away at war.

Antonio was born in Las Pasturas which is in the llano. The men who live there are *vaqueros* (cowboys), like his father. The llano is large and flat. It is very hot in the summer and very cold in the winter. The wind blows strongly and sometimes there are sandstorms.

Antonio's mother is from a farm family who live in the small village, El Puerto de los Lunas. She does not like the rough, hard life of the llano. After Antonio is born, she convinces his father to move to Guadalupe.

Antonio's parents knew Ultima in Las

Pasturas. She had helped with the birth of each of their children. Ultima is a *curandera* (a healer). Some believe healers have magical powers which are used for good. Others believe they are witches and fear them.

Because Ultima is now old and alone, Antonio's parents ask her to live with them. Antonio doesn't really know her, but he feels that he remembers her and that she will be important to his life.

Antonio begins the story writing as an adult. Then he flashes back to when he was seven years old and Ultima first came to live in his home. Antonio ends the story by bringing us back to his feelings now as an adult.

To help you read this story, we have broken it up into five parts. There are questions after each part to think about before reading on.

Perhaps the story will make you think about someone who was important to you when you were a child. Perhaps it will make you think about how your life is influenced by the place where you live.

Cast of Characters in
the Selection

ANTONIO
Antonio is the person who tells this story.

DEBORAH and THERESA
Antonio's older sisters.

GABRIEL
Antonio's father who comes from a family named Márez. They were cowboys who lived on the plain.

JASÓN
Jasón is Antonio's friend.

MARÍA
Antonio's mother who comes from a family named Luna. They were farmers who lived in the valley.

ULTIMA
Ultima is also known as la Grande, which means grandmother, or in this story, an old and wise woman.

Selected from

Bless Me, Ultima

Ultima came to stay with us the summer I was almost seven. When she came the beauty of the llano [plain] unfolded before my eyes, and the gurgling waters of the river sang to the hum of the turning earth. The magical time of childhood stood still, and the pulse of the living earth pressed its mystery into my living blood. She took my hand, and the silent, magic powers she possessed made beauty from the raw, sun-baked llano, the green river valley, and the blue bowl which was the white sun's home. My bare feet felt the throbbing earth and my body trembled with excitement. Time stood still, and it shared with me all that had been, and all that was to come. . . .

Questions for the Reader

1. Why do you think Ultima is important to Antonio?

2. How does the author let you know that he will be going back in time in the next part of the story?

———

Let me begin at the beginning. I do not mean the beginning that was in my dreams and the stories they whispered to me about my birth, and the people of my father and mother, and my three brothers —but the beginning that came with Ultima.

The attic of our home was partitioned into two small rooms. My sisters, Deborah and Theresa, slept in one and I slept in the small cubicle by the door. The wooden steps creaked down into a small hallway that led into the kitchen. From the top of the stairs I had a vantage point into the heart of our home, my mother's kitchen. From there I was to see the terrified face of Chávez when he brought the terrible news of the murder of the sheriff; I was to see the rebellion of my brothers against my father; and many times late at night I was to see Ultima returning from the llano where she gathered the herbs that can be harvested only in the light of the full moon by the careful hands of a curandera [healer].

That night I lay very quietly in my bed, and I heard my father and mother speak of Ultima.

"Está sola," my father said, "ya no queda gente en el pueblito de Las Pasturas —" ["She is alone," my father said, "no one is left in the little town of Las Pasturas —"]

He spoke in Spanish, and the village he mentioned was his home. My father had been a vaquero [cowboy] all his life, a calling as ancient as the coming of the Spaniard to Nuevo Méjico [New Mexico]. Even after the big rancheros [ranchers] and the tejanos [Texans] came and fenced the beautiful llano, he and those like him continued to work there, I guess because only in that wide expanse of land and sky could they feel the freedom their spirits needed.

"¡Qué lástima [what a pity]," my mother answered, and I knew her nimble fingers worked the pattern on the doily she crocheted for the big chair in the sala [living room].

I heard her sigh, and she must have shuddered too when she thought of Ultima living alone in the loneliness of the wide llano. My mother was not a woman of the llano, she was the daughter of a farmer. She could not see beauty in the llano and she could not understand the coarse men who lived half their lifetimes on horseback. After I was born in Las Pasturas she persuaded my father to leave the llano and bring her family to the town of Guadalupe where she said there would be opportunity and school for us. The move lowered my father in the esteem of his compadres [comrades], the other vaqueros of the llano who clung tenaciously to their way of life and freedom. There was no room to keep animals in town so my father had to sell his small herd, but he would not sell his horse so he gave it to a good friend, Benito Campos. But Campos could not keep the animal penned up because somehow the horse was very close to the spirit of the man, and so the horse was allowed to roam free and no vaquero on that llano would throw a lazo [lasso] on that horse. It was as if someone had died, and they turned their gaze from the spirit that walked the earth.

It hurt my father's pride. He saw less and less of his old compadres. He went to work on the highway and on Saturdays after they collected their pay he drank with his crew at the Longhorn, but he was never close to the men of the town. Some weekends the llaneros [plains-men] would come into town for sup-

plies and old amigos [friends] like
Bonney or Campos or the Gonzales
brothers would come by to visit. Then
my father's eyes lit up as they drank and
talked of the old days and told the old
stories. But when the western sun touched
the clouds with orange and gold the
vaqueros got in their trucks and headed
home, and my father was left to drink
alone in the long night. Sunday morning
he would get up very crudo [hungover]
and complain about having to go to early
mass.

"— She served the people all her life,
and now the people are scattered, driven
like tumbleweeds by the winds of war.
The war sucks everything dry," my father said solemnly, "it takes the young
boys overseas, and their families move
to California where there is work —"

"Ave María Purísima," my mother
made the sign of the cross for my three
brothers who were away at war. "Gabriel,"
she said to my father, "it is not right
that la Grande be alone in her old age —"

"No," my father agreed.

"When I married you and went to the llano to live with you and raise your family, I could not have survived without la Grande's help. Oh, those were hard years —"

"Those were good years," my father countered. But my mother would not argue.

"There isn't a family she did not help," she continued, "no road was too long for her to walk to its end to snatch somebody from the jaws of death, and not even the blizzards of the llano could keep her from the appointed place where a baby was to be delivered —"

"Es verdad [It's true]," my father nodded.

"She tended me at the birth of my sons —" And then I knew her eyes glanced briefly at my father. "Gabriel, we cannot let her live her last days in loneliness —"

"No," my father agreed, "it is not the way of our people."

"It would be a great honor to provide a home for la Grande," my mother murmured. My mother called Ultima la Grande out of respect. It meant the woman was old and wise.

"I have already sent word with Campos that Ultima is to come and live with us," my father said with some satisfaction. He knew it would please my mother.

"I am grateful," my mother said tenderly, "perhaps we can repay a little of the kindness la Grande has given to so many."

"And the children?" my father asked. I knew why he expressed concern for me and my sisters. It was because Ultima was a curandera, a woman who knew the herbs and remedies of the ancients, a miracle-worker who could heal the sick. And I had heard that Ultima could lift the curses laid by brujas [witches], that she could exorcise the evil the witches planted in people to make them sick. And because a curandera had this power she was misunderstood and often suspected of practicing witch-craft herself.

I shuddered and my heart turned cold at the thought. The cuentos [stories] of the people were full of the tales of evil done by brujas.

"She helped bring them into the world, she cannot be but good for the children," my mother answered.

"Está bien [That's good]," my father yawned, "I will go for her in the morning."

So it was decided that Ultima should come and live with us. I knew that my father and mother did good by providing a home for Ultima. It was the custom to provide for the old and the sick. There was always room in the safety and warmth of la familia [the family] for one more person, be that person stranger or friend.

Questions for the Reader

1. What have you learned about Antonio's father and his background? How has his life changed?

2. What have you learned about Antonio's mother and her background? How has her life changed?

3. Antonio seems to have mixed feelings about Ultima's arrival. How do you think his feelings will change?

———————

Most of the next part of the selection is set in special print called *italics*. The author uses it to let you know that there is something special or different about this part of the story. In this case, it is used to separate Antonio's dream from the rest the story.

It was warm in the attic, and as I lay quietly listening to the sounds of the house falling asleep and repeating a Hail Mary over and over in my thoughts, I drifted into the time of dreams. Once I had told my mother about my dreams and she said they were visions from God and she was happy, because her own dream was that I should grow up and become a priest. After that I did not tell her about my dreams, and they remained in me forever and ever ...

In my dream I flew over the rolling hills of the llano. My soul wandered over the dark plain until it came to a cluster of adobe huts. I recognized the village of Las Pasturas and my heart grew happy. One mud hut had a lighted window, and the vision of my dream swept me towards it to be witness at the birth of a baby.

I could not make out the face of the mother who rested from the pains of birth, but I could see the old woman in black who tended the just-arrived, steaming baby. She nimbly tied a knot on the cord that had connected the baby to its mother's blood, then quickly she bent and with her teeth she bit off the loose end. She wrapped the squirming baby and laid it at the mother's

*side, then she returned to cleaning the bed.
All linen was swept aside to be washed, but
she carefully wrapped the useless cord and
the afterbirth and laid the package at the
feet of the Virgin on the small altar. I
sensed that these things were yet to be
delivered to someone.*

*Now the people who had waited pa-
tiently in the dark were allowed to come in
and speak to the mother and deliver their
gifts to the baby. I recognized my mother's
brothers, my uncles from El Puerto de los
Lunas. They entered ceremoniously. A pa-
tient hope stirred in their dark, brooding
eyes.*

*This one will be a Luna, the old man
said, he will be a farmer and keep our
customs and traditions. Perhaps God will
bless our family and make the baby a priest.*

*And to show their hope they rubbed the
dark earth of the river valley on the baby's
forehead, and they surrounded the bed with
the fruits of their harvest so the small room
smelled of fresh green chile and corn, ripe
apples and peaches, pumpkins and green beans.*

Then the silence was shattered with the thunder of hoofbeats; vaqueros surrounded the small house with shouts and gunshots, and when they entered the room they were laughing and singing and drinking.

Gabriel, they shouted, you have a fine son! He will make a fine vaquero! And they smashed the fruits and vegetables that surrounded the bed and replaced them with a saddle, horse blankets, bottles of whiskey, a new rope, bridles, chapas [chaps], and an old guitar. And they rubbed the stain of earth from the baby's forehead because man was not to be tied to the earth but free upon it.

These were the people of my father, the vaqueros of the llano. They were an exuberant, restless people, wandering across the ocean of the plain.

We must return to our valley, the old man who led the farmers spoke. We must take with us the blood that comes after the birth. We will bury it in our fields to renew their fertility and to assure that the baby will follow our ways. He nodded for the old woman to deliver the package at the altar.

No! the llaneros protested, it will stay here! We will burn it and let the winds of the llano scatter the ashes.

It is blasphemy to scatter a man's blood on unholy ground, the farmers chanted. The new son must fulfill his mother's dream. He must come to El Puerto and rule over the Lunas of the valley. The blood of the Lunas is strong in him.

He is a Márez, the vaqueros shouted. His forefathers were conquistadores [conquerors], men as restless as the seas they sailed and as free as the land they conquered. He is his father's blood!

Curses and threats filled the air, pistols were drawn, and the opposing sides made ready for battle. But the clash was stopped by the old woman who delivered the baby.

Cease! she cried, and the men were quiet. I pulled this baby into the light of life, so I will bury the afterbirth and the cord that once linked him to eternity. Only I will know his destiny.

Questions for the Reader

1. Who do you think the baby is?

2. Who do you think the people are who are arguing over the baby?

3. Who do you think the old woman is?

The dream began to dissolve. When I opened my eyes I heard my father cranking the truck outside. I wanted to go with him, I wanted to see Las Pasturas, I wanted to see Ultima. I dressed hurriedly, but I was too late. The truck was bouncing down the goat path that led to the bridge and the highway.

I turned, as I always did, and looked down the slope of our hill to the green of the river, and I raised my eyes and saw the town of Guadalupe. Towering above the housetops and the trees of the town was the church tower. I made the sign of the cross on my lips. The only other building that rose above the house-

tops to compete with the church tower
was the yellow top of the schoolhouse.
This fall I would be going to school.

My heart sank. When I thought of
leaving my mother and going to school
a warm, sick feeling came to my stomach. To get rid of it I ran to the pens we
kept by the molino [mill] to feed the
animals. I had fed the rabbits that night
and they still had alfalfa and so I only
changed their water. I scattered some
grain for the hungry chickens and watched
their mad scramble as the rooster called
them to peck. I milked the cow and
turned her loose. During the day she
would forage along the highway where
the grass was thick and green, then she
would return at nightfall. She was a
good cow and there were very few times
when I had to run and bring her back
in the evening. Then I dreaded it, because she might wander into the hills
where the bats flew at dusk and there
was only the sound of my heart beating
as I ran and it made me sad and fright-
ened to be alone.

I collected three eggs in the chicken house and returned for breakfast.

"Antonio," my mother smiled and took the eggs and milk, "come and eat your breakfast."

I sat across the table from Deborah and Theresa and ate my atole [a drink made of cornmeal] and the hot tortilla [a flat cornmeal bread] with butter. I said very little. I usually spoke very little to my two sisters. They were older than I and they were very close. They usually spent the entire day in the attic, playing dolls and giggling. I did not concern myself with those things.

"Your father has gone to Las Pasturas," my mother chattered, "he has gone to bring la Grande." Her hands were white with the flour of the dough. I watched carefully. "—And when he returns, I want you children to show your manners. You must not shame your father or your mother—"

"Isn't her real name Ultima?" Deborah asked. She was like that, always asking grown-up questions.

"You will address her as la Grande," my mother said flatly. I looked at her and wondered if this woman with the black hair and laughing eyes was the woman who gave birth in my dream.

"Grande," Theresa repeated.

"Is it true she is a witch?" Deborah asked. Oh, she was in for it. I saw my mother whirl then pause and control herself.

"No!" she scolded. "You must not speak of such things! Oh, I don't know where you learn such ways—" Her eyes flooded with tears. She always cried when she thought we were learning the ways of my father, the ways of the Márez. "She is a woman of learning," she went on and I knew she didn't have time to stop and cry, "she has worked hard for all the people of the village. Oh, I would never have survived those hard years if it had not been for her—so show her respect. We are honored that she comes to live with us, understand?"

"Sí, mamá [Yes, mother]," Deborah said half willingly.

"Sí, mamá," Theresa repeated.

"Now run and sweep the room at the end of the hall. Eugene's room—" I heard her voice choke. She breathed a prayer and crossed her forehead. The flour left white stains on her, the four points of the cross. I knew it was because my three brothers were at war that she was sad, and Eugene was the youngest.

"Mamá." I wanted to speak to her. I wanted to know who the old woman was who cut the baby's cord.

"Sí." She turned and looked at me.

"Was Ultima at my birth?" I asked.

"¡Ay Dios mío [Oh, my God]!" my mother cried. She came to where I sat and ran her hand through my hair. She smelled warm, like bread. "Where do you get such questions, my son. Yes," she smiled, "la Grande was there to help me. She was there to help at the birth of all of my children—"

"And my uncles from El Puerto were there?"

"Of course," she answered, "my brothers have always been at my side when I needed them. They have always prayed that I would bless them with a——"

I did not hear what she said because I was hearing the sounds of the dream, and I was seeing the dream again. The warm cereal in my stomach made me feel sick.

"And my father's brother was there, the Márez' and their friends, the vaqueros——"

"Ay!" she cried out, "Don't speak to me of those worthless Márez and their friends!"

"There was a fight?" I asked.

"No," she said, "a silly argument. They wanted to start a fight with my brothers — that is all they are good for. Vaqueros, they call themselves, they are worthless drunks! Thieves! Always on the move, like gypsies, always dragging their families around the country like vagabonds——"

As long as I could remember she always raged about the Márez family and their friends. She called the village of Las Pasturas beautiful; she had gotten used to the loneliness, but she had never accepted its people. She was the daughter of farmers.

But the dream was true. It was as I had seen it. Ultima knew.

"But you will not be like them." She caught her breath and stopped. She kissed my forehead. "You will be like my brothers. You will be a Luna, Antonio. You will be a man of the people, and perhaps a priest." She smiled.

A priest, I thought, that was her dream. I was to hold mass on Sundays like Father Byrnes did in the church in town. I was to hear the confessions of the silent people of the valley, and I was to administer the holy Sacrament to them.

"Perhaps," I said.

"Yes," my mother smiled. She held me tenderly. The fragrance of her body was sweet.

"But then," I whispered, "who will hear my confession?"

"What?"

"Nothing," I answered. I felt a cool sweat on my forehead and I knew I had to run, I had to clear my mind of the dream. "I am going to Jasón's house," I said hurriedly and slid past my mother. I ran out the kitchen door, past the animal pens, towards Jasón's house. The white sun and the fresh air cleansed me.

On this side of the river there were only three houses. The slope of the hill rose gradually into the hills of juniper and mesquite and cedar clumps. Jasón's house was farther away from the river than our house. On the path that led to the bridge lived huge, fat Fío and his beautiful wife. Fío and my father worked together on the highway. They were good drinking friends.

"¡Jasón!" I called at the kitchen door. I had run hard and was panting. His mother appeared at the door.

"Jasón no está aquí [Jasón is not here],"

she said. All of the older people spoke only in Spanish, and I myself understood only Spanish. It was only after one went to school that one learned English.

"¿Dónde está [Where is he]?" I asked.

She pointed towards the river, northwest, past the railroad tracks to the dark hills. The river came through those hills and there were old Indian grounds there, holy burial grounds Jasón told me. There in an old cave lived his Indian. At least everybody called him Jasón's Indian. He was the only Indian of the town, and he talked only to Jasón. Jasón's father had forbidden Jasón to talk to the Indian, he had beaten him, he had tried in every way to keep Jasón from the Indian.

But Jasón persisted. Jasón was not a bad boy, he was just Jasón. He was quiet and moody, and sometimes for no reason at all wild, loud sounds came exploding from his throat and lungs. Sometimes I felt like Jasón, like I wanted to shout and cry, but I never did.

I looked at his mother's eyes and I

saw they were sad. "Thank you," I said, and returned home. While I waited for my father to return with Ultima I worked in the garden. Every day I had to work in the garden. Every day I reclaimed from the rocky soil of the hill a few more feet of earth to cultivate. The land of the llano was not good for farming, the good land was along the river. But my mother wanted a garden and I worked to make her happy. Already we had a few chile and tomato plants growing. It was hard work. My fingers bled from scraping out the rocks and it seemed that a square yard of ground produced a wheelbarrow full of rocks which I had to push down to the retaining wall.

Questions for the Reader

1. Why do you think Antonio asked his mother about his birth?

2. Why do you think Antonio felt "a cool sweat" on his forehead?

The sun was white in the bright blue sky. The shade of the clouds would not come until the afternoon. The sweat was sticky on my brown body. I heard the truck and turned to see it chugging up the dusty goat path. My father was returning with Ultima.

"¡Mamá!" I called. My mother came running out, Deborah and Theresa trailed after her.

"I'm afraid," I heard Theresa whimper.

"There's nothing to be afraid of," Deborah said confidently. My mother said there was too much Márez blood in Deborah. Her eyes and hair were very dark, and she was always running. She had been to school two years and she spoke only English. She was teaching Theresa and half the time I didn't understand what they were saying.

"Madre de Dios [Mother of God], but mind your manners!" my mother scolded. The truck stopped and she ran to greet

Ultima. "Buenos días le de Dios [God grant you a good day], Grande," my mother cried. She smiled and hugged and kissed the old woman.

"Ay, María Luna," Ultima smiled, "Buenos días te de Dios, a ti y a tu familia [God grant you a good day, to you and to your family]." She wrapped the black shawl around her hair and shoulders. Her face was brown and very wrinkled. When she smiled her teeth were brown. I remembered the dream.

"Come, come!" my mother urged us forward. It was the custom to greet the old. "Deborah!" my mother urged. Deborah stepped forward and took Ultima's withered hand.

"Buenos días, Grande," she smiled. She even bowed slightly. Then she pulled Theresa forward and told her to greet la Grande. My mother beamed. Deborah's good manners surprised her, but they made her happy, because a family was judged by its manners.

"What beautiful daughters you have

raised," Ultima nodded to my mother. Nothing could have pleased my mother more. She looked proudly at my father who stood leaning against the truck, watching and judging the introductions.

"Antonio," he said simply. I stepped forward and took Ultima's hand. I looked up into her clear brown eyes and shivered. Her face was old and wrinkled, but her eyes were clear and sparkling, like the eyes of a young child.

"Antonio," she smiled. She took my hand and I felt the power of a whirlwind sweep around me. Her eyes swept the surrounding hills and through them I saw for the first time the wild beauty of our hills and the magic of the green river. My nostrils quivered as I felt the song of the mockingbirds and the drone of the grasshoppers mingle with the pulse of the earth. The four directions of the llano met in me, and the white sun shone on my soul. The granules of sand at my feet and the sun and sky above me seemed to dissolve into one strange, complete being.

A cry came to my throat, and I wanted to shout it and run in the beauty I had found.

"Antonio." I felt my mother prod me. Deborah giggled because she had made the right greeting, and I who was to be my mother's hope and joy stood voiceless.

"Buenos días le de Dios, Ultima," I muttered. I saw in her eyes my dream. I saw the old woman who had delivered me from my mother's womb. I knew she held the secret of my destiny.

"¡Antonio!" My mother was shocked I had used her name instead of calling her Grande. But Ultima held up her hand.

"Let it be," she smiled. "This was the last child I pulled from your womb, María. I knew there would be something between us."

My mother who had started to mumble apologies was quiet. "As you wish, Grande," she nodded.

"I have come to spend the last days of

my life here, Antonio," Ultima said to me.

"You will never die, Ultima," I answered. "I will take care of you—" She let go of my hand and laughed. Then my father said, "pase [enter], Grande, pase. Nuestra casa es su casa [Our house is your house]. It is too hot to stand and visit in the sun—"

"Sí, sí," my mother urged. I watched them go in. My father carried on his shoulders the large blue-tin trunk which later I learned contained all of Ultima's earthly possessions, the black dresses and shawls she wore, and the magic of her sweet smelling herbs.

As Ultima walked past me I smelled for the first time a trace of the sweet fragrance of herbs that always lingered in her wake. Many years later, long after Ultima was gone and I had grown to be a man, I would awaken sometimes at night and think I caught a scent of her fragrance in the cool-night breeze.

Your Thoughts about the Selection from *Bless Me, Ultima*

1. What did you think of the selection from *Bless Me, Ultima*? Did you like it? Why?

2. Are there any ways that the events or people in the selection became important or special to you? Write or discuss why.

3. What parts of the selection were the most interesting? Why?

4. Was the selection what you expected it would be? Did it answer the questions you had before you began reading or listening? In what way did it?

5. Was there anything new or surprising to you in the selection? What?

QUESTIONS FOR THE READER

Thinking about the Story

1. Describe the people in the selection from *Bless Me, Ultima*. Which do you think is the most important? Why?

2. Ultima is a *curandera*. Find the parts of the story that describe how that makes her special or different.

3. In some fiction, *where* the story takes place is important. This story takes place in New Mexico. In what ways is this setting important or not important to the story?

4. As you were listening or reading, what were your thoughts as the story unfolded?

5. Were any parts of the selection difficult to understand? If so, you may want to read or listen to them again. You might think about why they were difficult.

Thinking about the Writing

1. How did Rudolfo Anaya help you see, hear, and feel what happened in the selection? Find the words, phrases, or sentences that you think did this the best.

2. Writers think about their stories' settings, characters, and events. In writing this story, which of these things do you think the author felt was most important? Find the parts of the story that support your opinion.

3. Which character was most interesting to you? How did Rudolfo Anaya help you learn about this person? Find the places in the selection where you learned the most about this person.

4. In the selection, the author uses dialogue. Dialogue can make a story stronger and more alive. Pick out some dialogue that you feel is strong, and explain how it helps the story.

5. The selection is seen through Antonio's eyes. He uses the words "I" and "me." How would the writing be different if the story was told from another character's point of view (such as Ultima's or María's), or from your own point of view?

6. In this story, Rudolfo Anaya creates an atmosphere of mystery. Right from the beginning, you have a feeling that there is something you do not understand. Go back to the story and see which parts make you feel this way.

Activities

1. Were there any words that were difficult for you in the selection from *Bless Me, Ultima*? Go back to these words and try to figure out their meanings. Discuss what you think each word means, and why you made that guess.

2. Are there any words new to you in the selection that you would like to remember? Discuss with your teacher or another student how you are going to remember each word. You could put them on file cards, or write them in your journal, or create a personal dictionary. Be sure to use each word in a sentence of your own.

3. How did you help yourself understand the selection? Did you ask yourself questions? What were they? Discuss these questions with other people who have read the same selection, or write about them in your journal.

4. Talking with other people about what you have read can increase your understanding of it. Discussion can help you organize your thoughts, get new ideas, and rethink your original ideas. Discuss your thoughts about the selection with someone else who has read it. Find out if your opinions are the same or different. See if your thoughts change as a result of this discussion.

5. If you like the selection, you might want to encourage someone else to read it. You could write a book review, or a letter to a friend you think might be interested in reading the book.

6. If you could talk to Rudolfo Anaya, what questions would you ask about his writing? You might want to write the questions in your journal.

7. Did reading the selection give you any ideas for your own writing? You might want to write about:

   • A person who was important to you when you were a child.
   • A dream you had that turned out to be real.
   • Something you had mixed emotions about and how you resolved them.

8. You might interview some people who come from backgrounds or cultures different than your own. Make a list of questions to ask them. Discuss what you have learned from these oral histories.

9. Is there something you kept thinking about after reading the selection? What? Write about why it is meaningful to you.

Spanish-English Glossary

amigos	friends
atole	a corn meal drink
brujas	witches
chapas	chaps (leather leggings)
compadres	comrades or friends
conquistadores	conquerors
crudo	hung over
cuentos	stories
curandera	a healer
la familia	the family
la Grande	grandmother or title of respect for an old wise woman
lazo	lasso
llano	plain or flat ground
llaneros	plainsmen
molino	mill
rancheros	ranchers
sala	living room
tejanos	Texans
tortilla	a flat cornmeal bread
vaquero	cowboy or herdsman

Seven series of good books for all readers:

WRITERS' VOICES

Selections from the works of America's finest and most popular writers, along with background information, maps, and other supplementary materials. Authors include: Kareem Abdul-Jabbar • Maya Angelou • Bill Cosby • Alex Haley • Stephen King • Loretta Lynn • Larry McMurtry • Amy Tan • Anne Tyler • Abigail Van Buren • Alice Walker • Tom Wolfe, and many others.

NEW WRITERS' VOICES

Anthologies and individual narratives by adult learners. A wide range of topics includes home and family, prison life, and meeting challenges. Many titles contain photographs or illustrations.

OURWORLD

Selections from the works of well-known science writers, along with related articles and illustrations. Authors include David Attenborough and Carl Sagan.

FOR YOUR INFORMATION

Clearly written and illustrated works on important self-help topics. Subjects include: Eating Right • Managing Stress • Getting Fit • About AIDS • Getting Good Health Care, among others.

TIMELESS TALES

Classic myths, legends, folk tales, and other stories from around the world, with special illustrations.

SPORTS

Fact-filled books on baseball, football, basketball, and boxing, with lots of action photos. With read-along tapes narrated by Phil Rizzuto, Frank Gifford, Dick Vitale, and Sean O'Grady.

SULLY GOMEZ MYSTERIES

Fast-paced detective series starring Sully Gomez and the streets of Los Angeles.

WRITE FOR OUR FREE COMPLETE CATALOG:

SIGNAL HILL

Signal Hill Publications
P.O. Box 131
Syracuse, NY 13210-0131